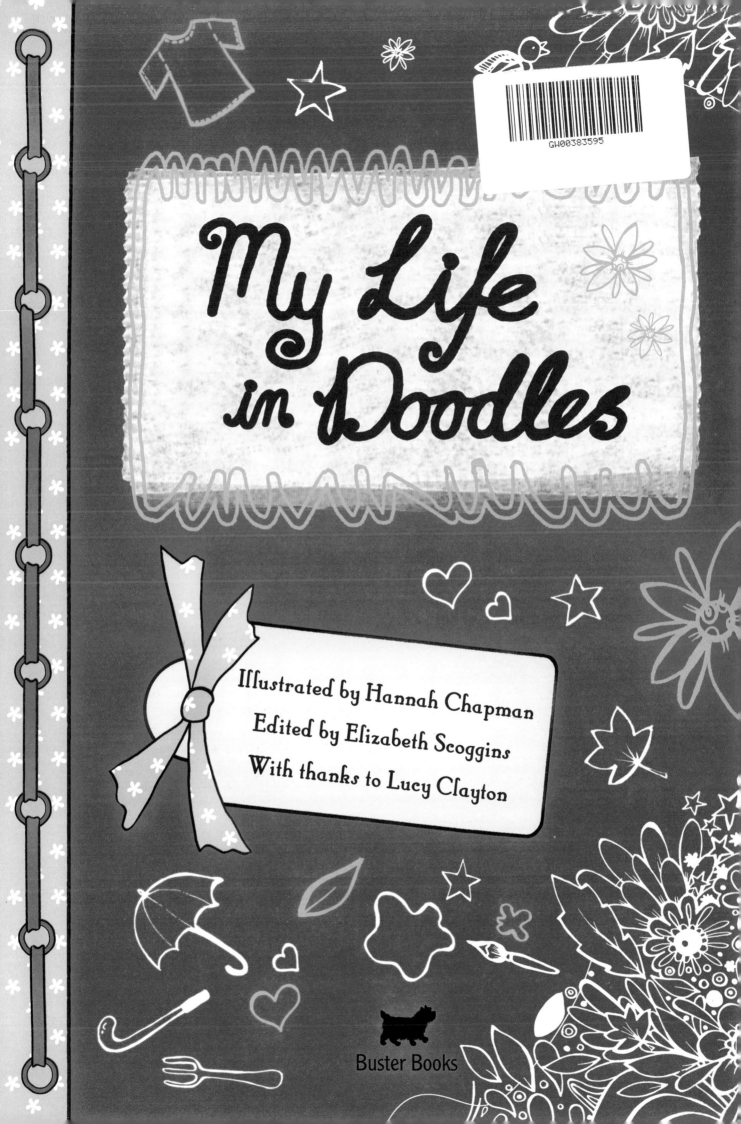

My Life in Doodles

Illustrated by Hannah Chapman

Edited by Elizabeth Scoggins

With thanks to Lucy Clayton

Buster Books

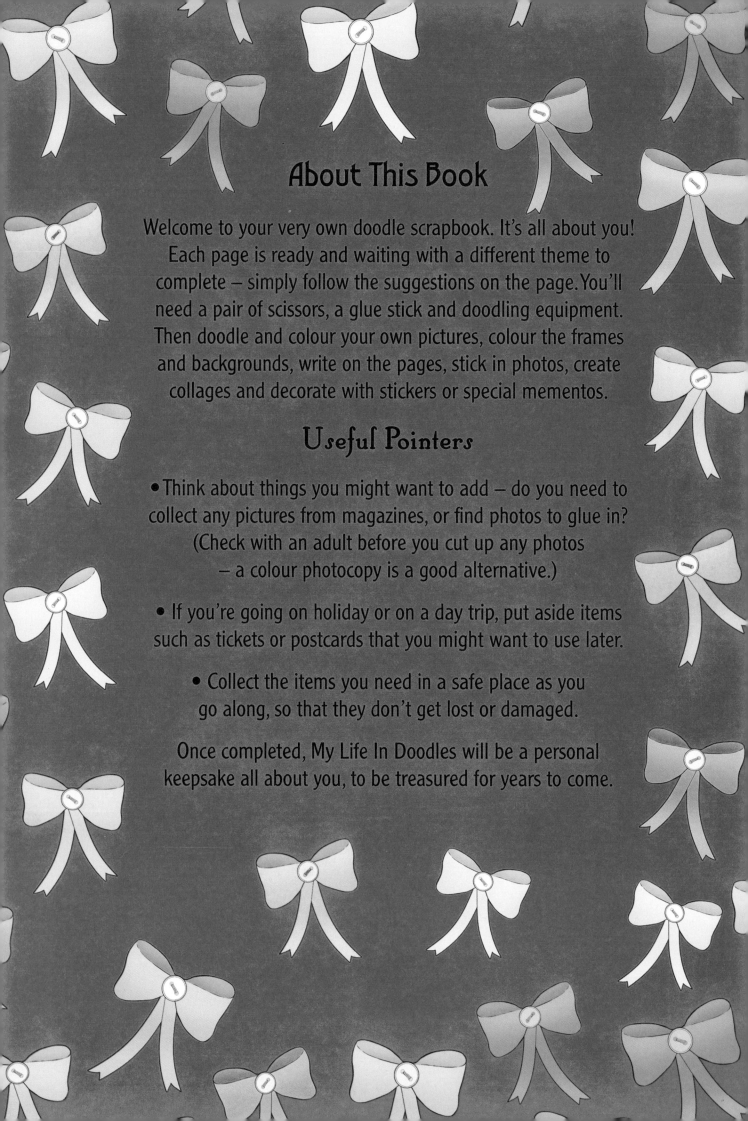

About This Book

Welcome to your very own doodle scrapbook. It's all about you!
Each page is ready and waiting with a different theme to
complete – simply follow the suggestions on the page. You'll
need a pair of scissors, a glue stick and doodling equipment.
Then doodle and colour your own pictures, colour the frames
and backgrounds, write on the pages, stick in photos, create
collages and decorate with stickers or special mementos.

Useful Pointers

• Think about things you might want to add – do you need to
collect any pictures from magazines, or find photos to glue in?
(Check with an adult before you cut up any photos
– a colour photocopy is a good alternative.)

• If you're going on holiday or on a day trip, put aside items
such as tickets or postcards that you might want to use later.

• Collect the items you need in a safe place as you
go along, so that they don't get lost or damaged.

Once completed, My Life In Doodles will be a personal
keepsake all about you, to be treasured for years to come.

A Little Bit About Me

Use this page to introduce yourself. Add your details in the spaces provided and colour in the buttons in the background. Once you've finished, add your signature at the bottom of the page.

My Fact File:

My name is . . . .

My friends call me . . . .

I am . . . . years old

My birthday is on . . . .

I live in . . . .

The colour of my eyes is . . . .

The colour of my hair is . . . .

This Is Me Now:

Draw a picture of how you look right now.

This Is Me As A Baby:

Find a photo of you as a baby to glue here.

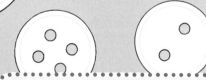

Sign here:

. . . .

Even More About Me

This book really is all about you, so don't be shy, tick the boxes and fill in the blanks to record your opinions and your personality for years to come!

My Mood

Usually I feel:

Completely cheerful ☐

Quite grumpy ☐

Lively and loud ☐

Quiet and thoughtful ☐

A little bit sad ☐

.... ☐

First Impressions

People think of me as:

Funny ☐

Trustworthy ☐

A good friend ☐

Embarrassingly loud ☐

Quite shy ☐

.... ☐

My Dream

If I could do anything, I would:

Climb a mountain ☐

Be lead singer in a band ☐

Win the lottery ☐

Win a gold medal ☐

.... ☐

The person I most admire is:

....

....

....

Because:

....

....

These are a few of my favourite things.

In the heart, write, add doodles or pictures cut out of magazines of each of your favourite things right now.

Describe Me

Which of these words describe you?
(Circle as many as you like.)

happy   funny   shy   quirky   sleepy

outgoing   clever   silly   bubbly   lucky

talented   surprising   cool

stylish   brave

Naming Names

If I could be called anything, my name would be:

. . . .

. . . .

My Dream Bedroom

You might be lucky enough to have your own room, or perhaps you share with a brother or sister, but how would you have your room, ideally? Use this page to plan your dream room.

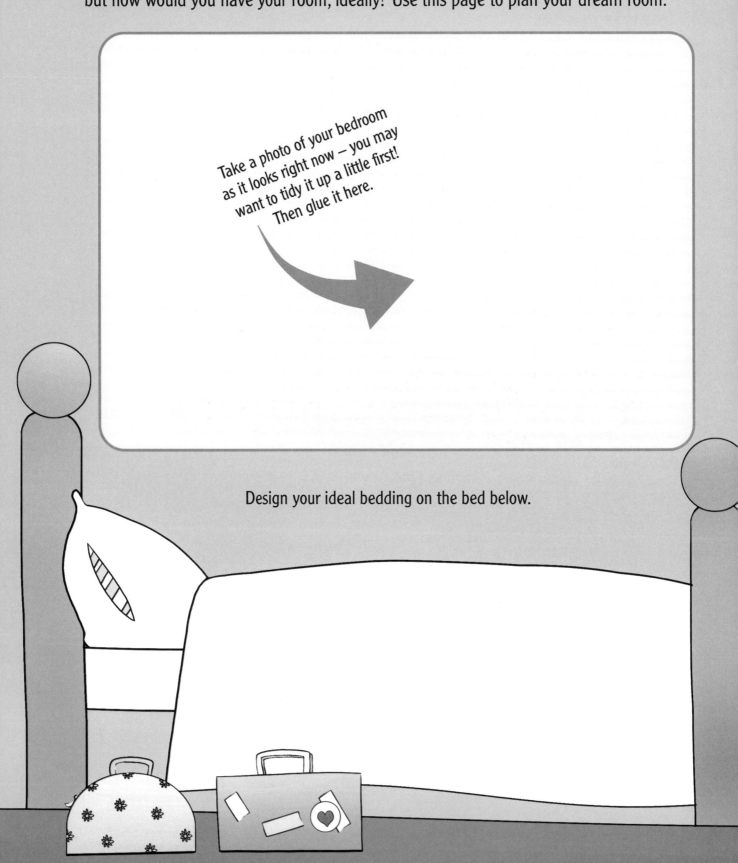

Take a photo of your bedroom as it looks right now — you may want to tidy it up a little first! Then glue it here.

Design your ideal bedding on the bed below.

What Would You Wish For?

Use these suggestions to create a collage of your dream bedroom in the space below.

• What's On The Walls?

Look in magazines and catalogues for your ideal wallpaper or paint colour. Start your collage by glueing this on in the background.

• Finest Furniture

Look for a picture of a bed, a wardrobe and a chest of drawers that you love. Cut them out and glue them on over your walls.

• Best Bedding

Choose your ideal duvet and pillow covers and place them on your chosen bed.

• Lighting

Pick lampshades and lights that you love.

• Finishing Touches

Cushions and rugs can complete the look of your bedroom – find your favourites and glue them in place to finish your dream bedroom.

Make a collage of your dream bedroom, using the suggestions above to get you started.

School's Cool

Fill this page with your favourite things about school and get your friends to help, too.
Remember to add your own finishing touches to the background.

School Statistics

My school is called:

....

I am in class:

....

My best subject is:

....

My worst subject is:

....

My favourite teacher is:

....

My favourite lunch is:

....

At break time, I like to:

....

After school, I like to:

....

School's Cool Because:

I get to learn new things.

I see my friends every day.

I get to eat school dinner.

I can play all through lunch.

My teacher is nice.

Doodle what your school's badge looks like here.

This Book Belongs To:

Ask each of your friends to sign their name
on the cover of this exercise book.

Spring Watch

Spring is a time for fresh starts, with new flowers growing, a new term at school and plenty to look forward to. Add your own colours to the spring flowers, following the instructions to complete your spring-themed page.

Fill the field with lambs and colour the picture.

What Are Your Favourite Signs Of Spring?

Baby animals

New leaves on trees

Warmer weather

Flowers opening

Doodle the scene from your bedroom window during spring.

Press A Spring Flower

Choose your favourite spring flower and press it between the pages of this book, in the frame on the right.

Complete the frame with your own choice of colours to match the flower you have chosen.

A Day To Remember

No matter what time of year your birthday is, it's your special day,
and time to celebrate! Use this page to remind you what happened this year.

Three Wishes:

When you blow out your birthday candles, you can make a wish. This year, what would your top three wishes be? Shhh! Don't tell anyone, or they won't come true!

1. . . . .

2. . . . .

3. . . . .

Fill the birthday party with balloons and streamers. Can you add some guests?

Birthday Surprises

What gifts were you given, and who were they from?

I got a ....

from ....

I got a ....

from ....

I got a ....

from ....

I got a ....

from ....

I got a ....

from ....

Don't forget to say
a special 'thank you' for each one!

Doodle your party outfit here.

Add your favourite colours to the gift-box border.

Design your ideal birthday cake here.

At The Movies

A trip to the cinema is a real treat – and there's nothing like seeing the latest film on the big screen. Use this page to make a record of your best cinema memories.

How Often Do You Go To The Cinema?

Twice a week ☐

Once a week ☐

Twice a month ☐

Once a month ☐

Occasionally ☐

What Are Your Favourite Types Of Film?

Romance ☐

Action ☐

Adventure ☐

Spooky stories ☐

True-life stories ☐

Superheroes ☐

Friendship

Which films have you been to see lately? Write their titles on the cinema listing below:

NOW SHOWING

What Are Your Best Cinema Snacks?

Popcorn ☐

Nachos ☐

Ice cream ☐

Chocolate ☐

Sweets ☐

Who have they gone to the cinema with?

The last film that made me laugh was:

· · · · · · · · · · · · · · · ·

· · · · · · · · · · · · · · · ·

The last film that made me cry was:

· · · · · · · · · · · · · · · ·

· · · · · · · · · · · · · · · ·

The last film that made me jump was:

· · · · · · · · · · · · · · · ·

· · · · · · · · · · · · · · · ·

The last film that made me yawn was:

· · · · · · · · · · · · · · · ·

· · · · · · · · · · · · · · · ·

The last film that made me want to leave was:

· · · · · · · · · · · · · · · ·

· · · · · · · · · · · · · · · ·

Glue the ticket for the best film you have seen at the cinema recently here.

Summer Sensations

Time off school, hot weather and endless days of fun can make summer one of the best times of year. Use this page to remind you of your favourite days and best moments. On the next page, you will be able to record what happens if you go away.

Use this space to doodle a picture or glue a photo of your favourite summer day.

Summer Holiday Record

How many weeks did you have away from school?

....

What did you do in the school holidays?

....

....

....

....

What did you wish you had done in the school holidays?

....

....

....

....

Which Of These Is The Best Thing About Summer?

Sunshine ☐

Going to the beach ☐

Summer clothes ☐

Wearing flip-flops ☐

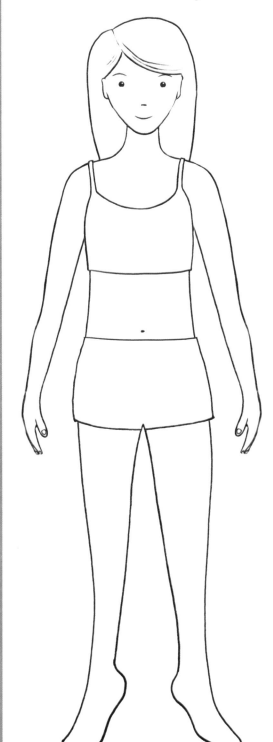

Cut out pictures of your favourite summer outfits from magazines.

Glue them on the model to create a sensational summer outfit for her.

Fashion Passions

Clothes can make you feel warm in the winter and cooler in the summer.
They can make you part of a group or stand out from the crowd.
Whatever your fashion favourites, this is the place to make a record of what
your ideal style is right here, right now.

My Own Clothes Show

My favourite outfit is:

. . . .

My worst outfit ever was:

. . . .

The colour that suits me best is:

. . . .

My favourite type of shoe is:

. . . .

At the weekend, I like to wear:

. . . .

After school, I like to wear:

. . . .

When I am older, I want to wear:

. . . .

I couldn't live without my:

. . . .

Glue a photo of yourself in your favourite outfit here.

Use this space to create your perfect outfit by cutting out your favourite items from old magazines.

Glue each item into the space provided then draw them on to your very own fashion model.

A cool hat

A pretty top, or dress

A stylish scarf, or necklace

Cool trousers, funky tights or leggings

Cool socks

Perfect shoes

Holiday Happenings

While you are on your holidays, keep an eye out for things you could add to this page. For example, you might visit a country that has unusual stamps, or you might eat some sweets with interesting wrappers. Stick the stamp, the wrapper and anything else that reminds you of your trip, onto this page.

10 Things I Can't Do Without:

When you go away, which items do you absolutely have to take?

1. . . . .

2. . . . .

3. . . . .

4. . . . .

5. . . . .

6. . . . .

7. . . . .

8. . . . .

9. . . . .

10. . . . .

Glue the best stamp you have found here.

On your travels, you may have tried new foods. Doodle your favourite new meal here.

Choose your favourite postcard
from your trip and glue it here.

Then decorate the frame
with doodles of pretty shells
and pebbles.

Give these shells colours bright enough to shout about.

Glue a ticket for a trip
you took here.

More About Me!

Follow the line of footprints and fill in the most special events of your life so far.
These might include your first steps, your earliest memory, your first party dress, your first day at
school or prizes you have won. Label each event and write the date that each one happened.
Doodle a picture or glue in a photograph to show each event. The first one has been done for you.

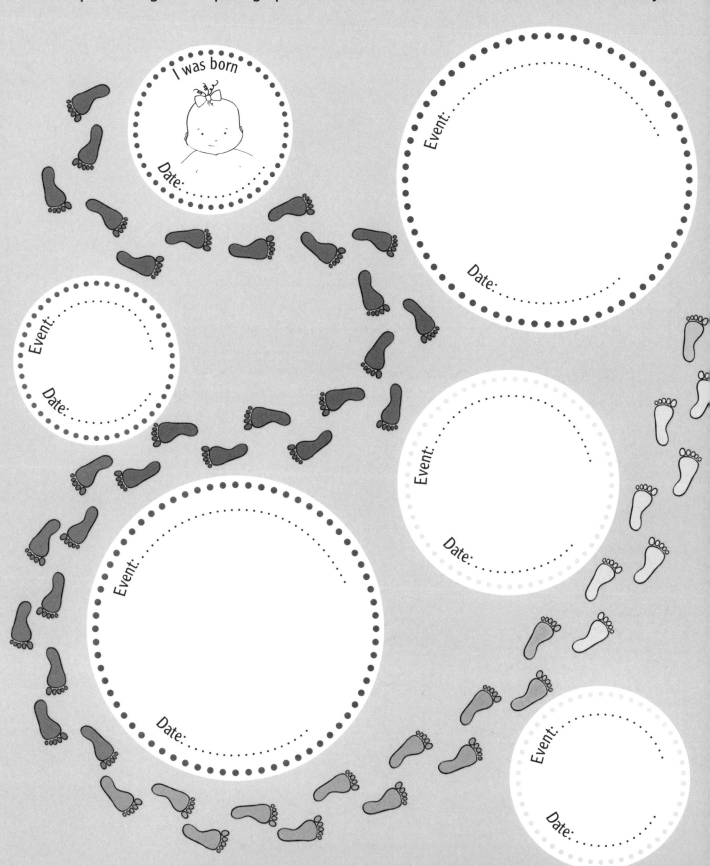

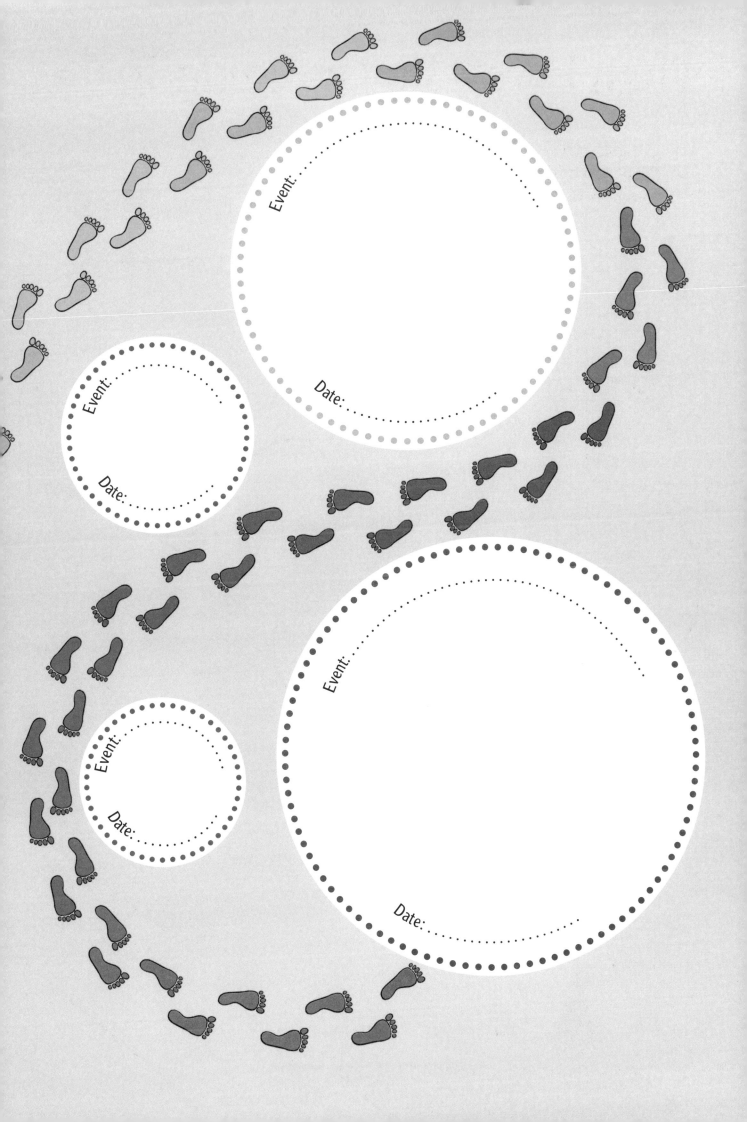

Event: ......

Date: ......

Event: ......

Date: ......

Event: ......

Date: ......

Event: ......

Date: ......

When I Grow Up I'm Going To Be...

When you were very little, you might have wanted to be an astronaut or a ballerina. What is your dream job right now? Use this page to record your ambitions for the future.

Best And Worst

The worst job I can imagine is:

. . . .

The best job I can imagine is:

. . . .

Complete the rainbow in your favourite colours.

Doodle yourself doing your dream job.

My Top-Five Careers:

Lots of people have more than one sort of job in their lives - you might be able to imagine yourself doing all sorts of things. Think of five that you would most like to try and put them in order with your favourite at number one.

1. ....

2. ....

3. ....

4. ....

5. ....

What do your parents do? Doodle them doing their jobs here.

All About My Future

Years from now, perhaps when you're a famous designer, a TV star or a sports champion, you'll be able to look back at this page to recall your predictions. What does your future hold?

Ten Years From Now

In this frame, doodle a picture of what you think you might look like ten years into the future. Will your hair be different, will you look much older?

Add more weird futuristic buildings to the background.

The World's Future

Which of these things do you think will happen in the future?

Everyone will travel in space ☐

People will live on other planets ☐

We will meet aliens ☐

There will be flying cars ☐

People will be wearing computerised clothing ☐

Everyone will read minds ☐

I will travel by jetpack ☐

I will be able to see television inside my head ☐

I will have a house under water ☐

I will have a pet robot ☐

My Future

Which of these things do you think will happen to you in the future?

I will get top marks ☐

I will be in the newspaper ☐

I will be on television ☐

I will win a talent show ☐

I will write a book ☐

I will go travelling ☐

I will go to university ☐

I will fall in love ☐

I will get married ☐

I will have children ☐

What do you think you will see from your bedroom window in the future? Doodle it here.

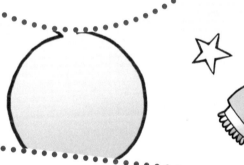

My Top-Five Ambitions:

What five things would you most like to have achieved, ten years from now? Whether it's to learn how to fly a plane, discover a cure for the common cold or win an Olympic gold medal, list your ambitions below.

1. ....

2. ....

3. ....

4. ....

5. ....

My Favourite Music

When you want to relax, your favourite song can help you unwind
– when you want some energy, you can put on something upbeat and dance!
There are so many different kinds of music – whatever you enjoy listening to,
use this space to remember it and put your mark on the music world in doodles.

Music, Please!

My favourite type of music is:

....

My favourite group is:

....

My favourite artist is:

....

I wish I could sing like:

....

The first music I bought was:

....

My favourite song is:

....

If I could meet any musician,
alive or dead, it would be:

....

The person/group I would most like
to see play live is:

....

Mad On Music

The instrument I am learning to play is:

....

The instrument I would like to learn to play is:

....

I can/can't read music. (Delete one.)

I am a good/okay/bad singer. (Delete two.)

My friends think the singer I sound like is:

....

Add yourself to the group!

If you were in a band, what would it be called?

Design a logo for your band here.

A Forest Of Friendship

Lots of the friends that you make now could be your friends for life.
This is the place to make your friendship memories last for ever, too.
Add your friends to the Friendship Forest, then complete the rest of the page.

The Best Of Friends

Find your favourite photo of you and your best friend. Glue it here.

My Best Friend Is:

....

We Both Love:

....

We Both Hate:

....

My Friends And I Like To:

Laugh all the time ☐

Sing songs ☐

Tell stories ☐

Play games ☐

Go to the park ☐

Have sleepovers ☐

Do homework together ☐

Go to the cinema ☐

Go to clubs together ☐

Think of as many words as you can to describe the best things about your friends, then write them in the circle.

The friend I have known longest is:
....
....

My newest friend is:
....
....

Who's Hiding In The Trees?

Find a selection of photos of your friends and carefully cut around their faces. Then glue each one in position over the faces of the tree people to make a forest of friends!

Read All About It

For anyone that loves to read, there's nothing like escaping into the world of books, magazines and comics. Whether you prefer to read stories or factual books or enjoy writing your own, there's a whole world to explore. Use this page to record your favourites.

My Life Story

Lots of people who have interesting lives write what is called an autobiography. They choose interesting or funny titles that tell you a bit about them. What would you call yours?

....

....

....

My Top-Five Books:

1. ....

2. ....

3. ....

4. ....

5. ....

What's In A Name?

Why not dream up your pen name (the name you would use as a writer). One way to decide is to use the name of your favourite flower and the name of the street you live on as your first and second names. What would yours be?

....

Find the perfect photo to use as your author picture and glue it here.

Cool Cover Designer

When you choose a book, the cover is the first thing you see.
Use this space to design a cover for one of your favourite books,
or even one that you want to write yourself.

The place I am most likely to be found reading in is:

....

....

My favourite author is:

....

....

When I am older, I would like to read:

....

....

And The Award Goes To ...

Every group of friends is made up of different characters – one might be loud, one funny, one quiet and another serious. Whatever they're like, there's an award for everyone. Which of your friends would you give the following awards to? Write a name under each one.

☆

Finish her glamorous dress for the awards ceremony.

Friend Least Likely To
Be On Time:

....

....

☆

Most Reliable Friend:

....

....

Funniest Friend:

....

....

Biggest Drama Queen:
....
....
....
....

Best Secret-Keeper:
....
....

Friend Most Likely To
Rescue An Animal:
....
....
....

Colour and
decorate the
envelopes.

Sweetest Person:
....
....
....

Most Stylish Friend:
....
....
....

Friend Most Likely To
Fall In Love:
....
....
....

Friend Most Likely To
Become Famous:
....
....
....

Best Celebrations Ever

When it's time to celebrate, everyone does something different – whether it's a birthday, a wedding or a street party, how do your family and friends mark important occasions? Make a record of your favourite parties and special events here.

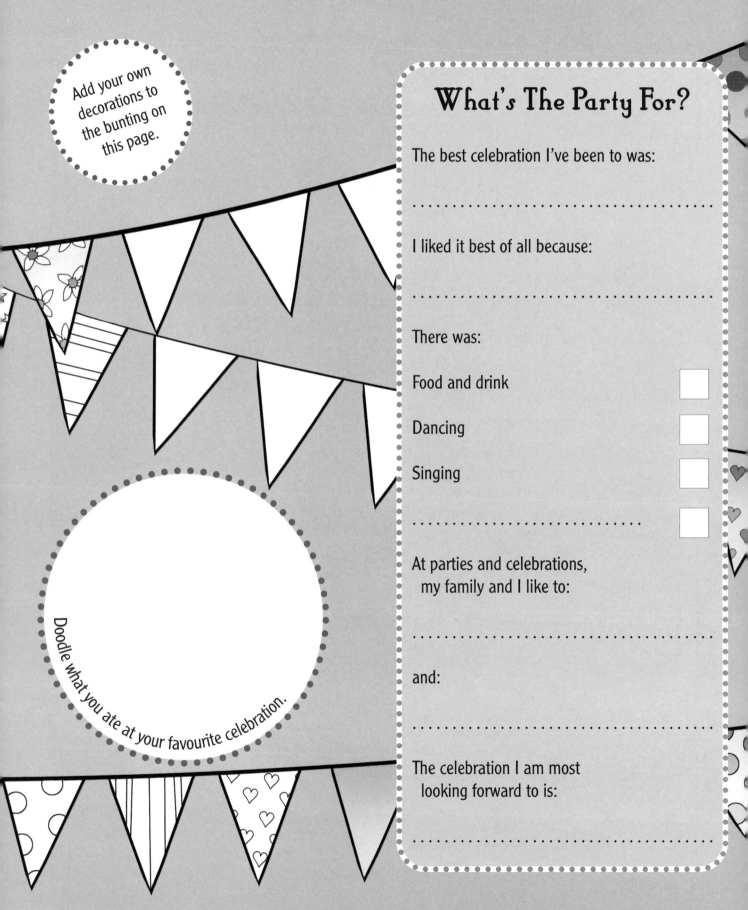

Add your own decorations to the bunting on this page.

Doodle what you ate at your favourite celebration.

What's The Party For?

The best celebration I've been to was:

....

I liked it best of all because:

....

There was:

Food and drink ☐

Dancing ☐

Singing ☐

.... ☐

At parties and celebrations, my family and I like to:

....

and:

....

The celebration I am most looking forward to is:

....

Party Time!

Use this space to design an invitation to the perfect party. What are you celebrating?
Where will it take place? What should people wear?

The Best Party Ever!

Glue your favourite party photo here, then decorate the frame to match.

Family Days

When you and your family go for a special day out, you're sure to come back with tons of memories of the time you've spent together. Use this space to help you record those memories.

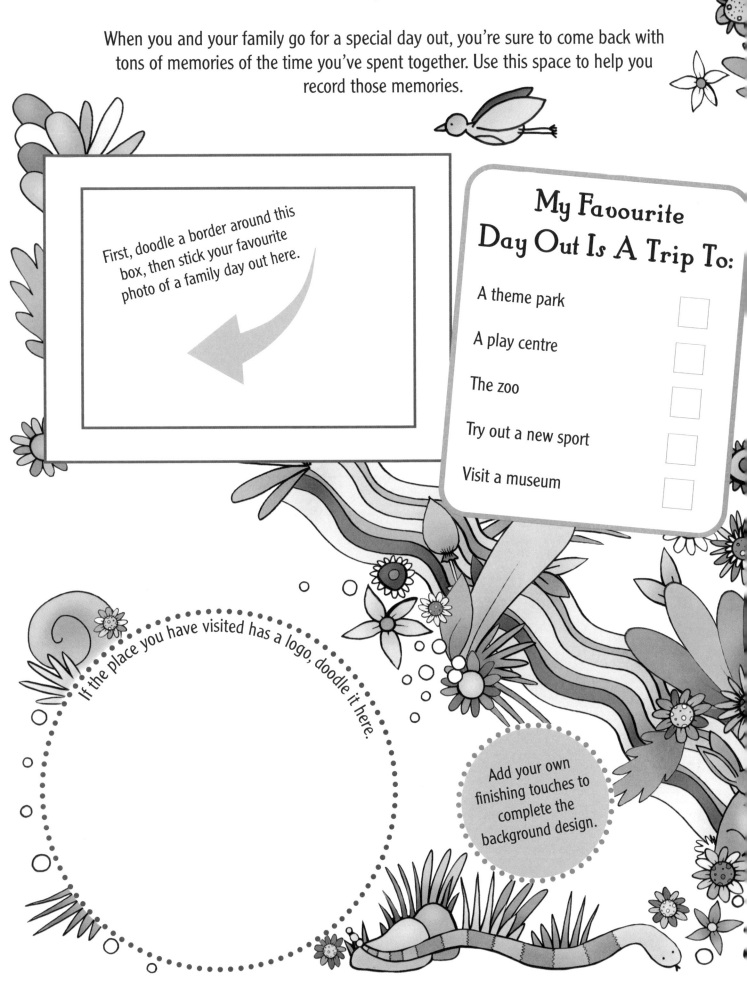

First, doodle a border around this box, then stick your favourite photo of a family day out here.

My Favourite Day Out Is A Trip To:

A theme park ☐

A play centre ☐

The zoo ☐

Try out a new sport ☐

Visit a museum ☐

If the place you have visited has a logo, doodle it here.

Add your own finishing touches to complete the background design.

Draw your family on the train.

Glue any tickets
you bought here.

In Your Dreams

When you're snuggled up in bed, there's nothing nicer than drifting off to dreamland, where anything can happen. Use this quilted page to describe your dreams, add your own patterns to the empty quilt squares, then colour them in.

Good Dreams You Have Had:

Flying through the air

Winning a prize

Knowing all the answers in class

Coming first in a race

An amazing holiday

Bad Dreams You Have Had:

Falling and waking with a jump

Missing the bus

Starting a new school

Losing your homework

Getting an answer wrong

Use the space below to describe the best dream you have ever had.

....

....

....

....

....

....

....

....

....

....

My Family Tree

Cut out photos or draw pictures of your family members to complete this family tree. Add their names in the box below, then fill the page with colour.

I Look Most Like:

My mum ☐

My dad ☐

Who's Who?

My dad's name:

....

His dad's name:

....

His mum's name:

My mum's name:

....

Her dad's name:

....

Her mum's name:

Fill the sky
with birds.

Grandparents

Parents

Me

Do you have any brothers, sisters or pets? Add them beneath the tree.

Awesome Autumn

When leaves start to turn and the weather begins to change, you know that winter is on its way, but there is a lot to enjoy about autumn first.

My Favourite Autumn Activities Are:

Kicking up piles of leaves ☐

Melting marshmallows ☐

Walking in the woods ☐

Watching fireworks ☐

Halloween ☐

Playing conkers ☐

Doodle an autumn-themed border around this box, then stick your favourite autumn photo or picture from a magazine here.

Doodle the scene from your bedroom window during autumn.

My Favourite Autumn Leaf

Glue a leaf that you have found on an autumn walk here.

Colour these leaves in your favourite autumnal colours.

The Street Where I Live

Whether you live in a house or a flat, or even somewhere more unusual, such as a boat or a caravan, the place where you live is home – what's yours like? Colour and complete the houses on the street below. You could even doodle what's inside the houses.

Make this page your own.

Glue a photo of where you live right now, here.

What Would Your Dream Home Be:

A stylish apartment ☐

A pretty cottage ☐

A huge mansion ☐

A castle or a palace ☐

A houseboat ☐

Where I live right now ☐

Doodle your dream view here.

Who's At Home In Your Home?

I live with:

....

....

....

....

Old Or New?

Do you know when your home was built? Ask an adult to check for you and write it here:

....

Things To Do

You might be sporty, artistic, studious, creative, or all of these things and more!
Whatever you enjoy doing in your spare time, take some of that time
to fill this page with memories.

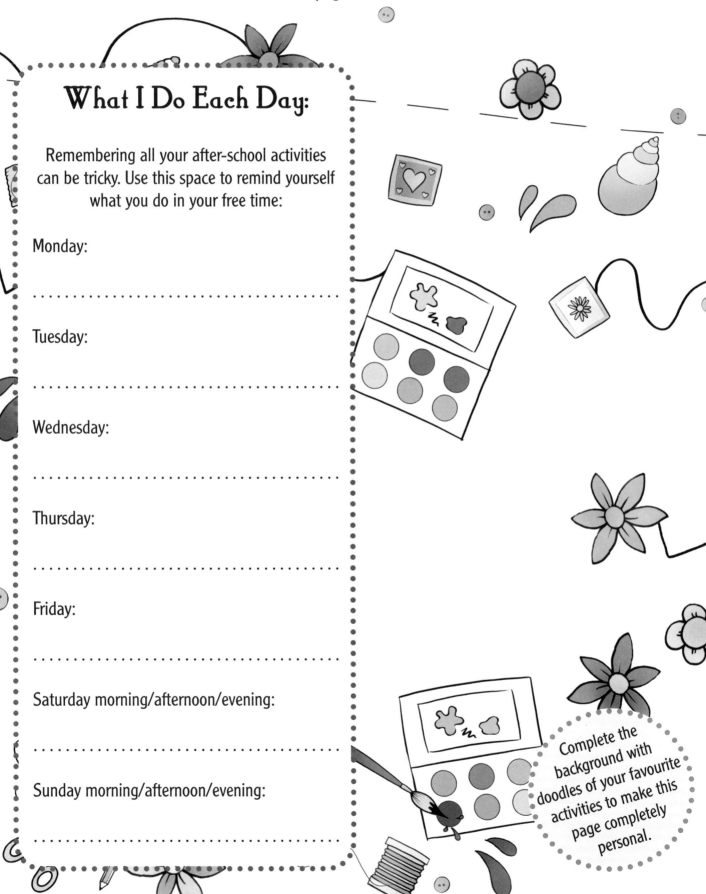

What I Do Each Day:

Remembering all your after-school activities can be tricky. Use this space to remind yourself what you do in your free time:

Monday:

....

Tuesday:

....

Wednesday:

....

Thursday:

....

Friday:

....

Saturday morning/afternoon/evening:

....

Sunday morning/afternoon/evening:

....

Complete the background with doodles of your favourite activities to make this page completely personal.

Find a photo or doodle a picture of you doing your favourite activity or hobby and glue it here. Then decorate the border.

My Favourite Activities And Hobbies Are:

Drawing and doodling

Ballet

Gymnastics

Playing music

Football

Tennis

Horse riding

Playing computer games

Cooking

Doing crafts

Martial arts

. . . .

Imagine you've won a medal for your favourite activity. Doodle what it would look like here.

Food Favourites

Whether you love crisps and dislike cake, or can't stand celery but would eat apples every day if you could – food is something that you definitely have an opinion about. Use this page to record your food likes and dislikes and add your own personal touches.

Rate These Foods By Circling The Cherries

	Delicious	Yummy	Okay	Not Nice	Gross
Pizza					
Cupcakes					
Apples					
Ice Cream					
Oranges					

Spend some time gathering pictures of your favourite foods from magazines, then make a collage that's good enough to eat!

My favourite thing to eat is:

....

My least favourite thing to eat is:

....

I would like to try:

....

My Best Recipe Yet

What's the best recipe you have ever made yourself?
Write out how you made it here:

....

....

....

....

....

....

Doodle how it turned out here.

Celebrity Crush!

Do you have a favourite TV star, singer or sports star?
Do you think about what you might say if you met them in real life?
If so, then this is the page to make a record of your celebrity crush. No blushing!

My Top-Five Crushes:

1. ....

2. ....

3. ....

4. ....

5. ....

Use the space below to describe your ideal first date:

....

....

....

....

....

....

....

....

....

Prince Charming

Find a picture of your top celebrity crush in a magazine. Cut it out and glue it in place here. Don't worry if you don't like what your crush is wearing – just choose a better outfit, cut it out and glue it over the top!

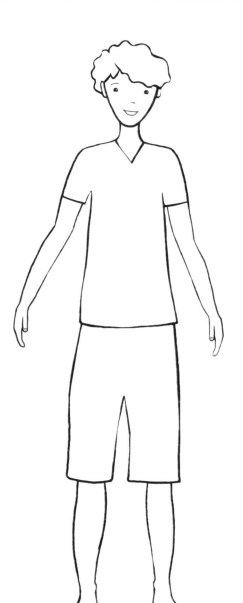

Design your own heart-shaped sweet.

Add pinks, reds and purples to the pretty hearts.

Top Secret!

If you're good at keeping secrets, your friends might tell you lots of important things that they trust you to keep to yourself – don't write any of those here! Instead, use this page to make a record of your own best secrets, whether it's your most embarrassing moment, or your secret crush. If you like, you can tape this page shut when you're finished!

Secret Keeper?

My friends know that I am good/bad at keeping secrets. (Delete one.)

Shh!

Turn Back Time?

The one thing I wish that I hadn't done is:

. . . .

. . . .

. . . .

Shh!

Superhero For A Day?

If I could have any secret power, it would be:

. . . .

. . . .

. . . .

Shh!

Design your own superpower logo here.

Wish The Floor Would Swallow You Up?

My most embarrassing moment was:

. . . .

. . . .

. . . .

Shh!

When I blush, I go this colour! (Colour in the circle.)

Times Tells!

The longest I have ever kept a secret is:

. . . .

Shh!

What Happens Next?

If I could look into the future, I would try find out:

. . . .

. . . .

. . . .

Shh!

Who Knows?

If I could read minds, I would try to find out:

. . . .

. . . .

. . . .

Shh!

Loves Me, Loves Me Not?

My secret crush is:

. . . .

. . . .

Shh!

Travel Plans

If you could visit anywhere in the world — or even beyond — where would you choose to go? Use this page to plan your future travels.

Design a ticket to your dream destination.

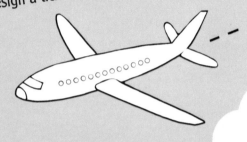

Find a picture of your number one destination in a magazine — cut it out and glue it here, then decorate the frame.

Top-Ten Destinations:

These are the places I would most like to visit in the future:

1. ....

2. ....

3. ....

4. ....

5. ....

6. ....

7. ....

8. ....

9. ....

10. ....

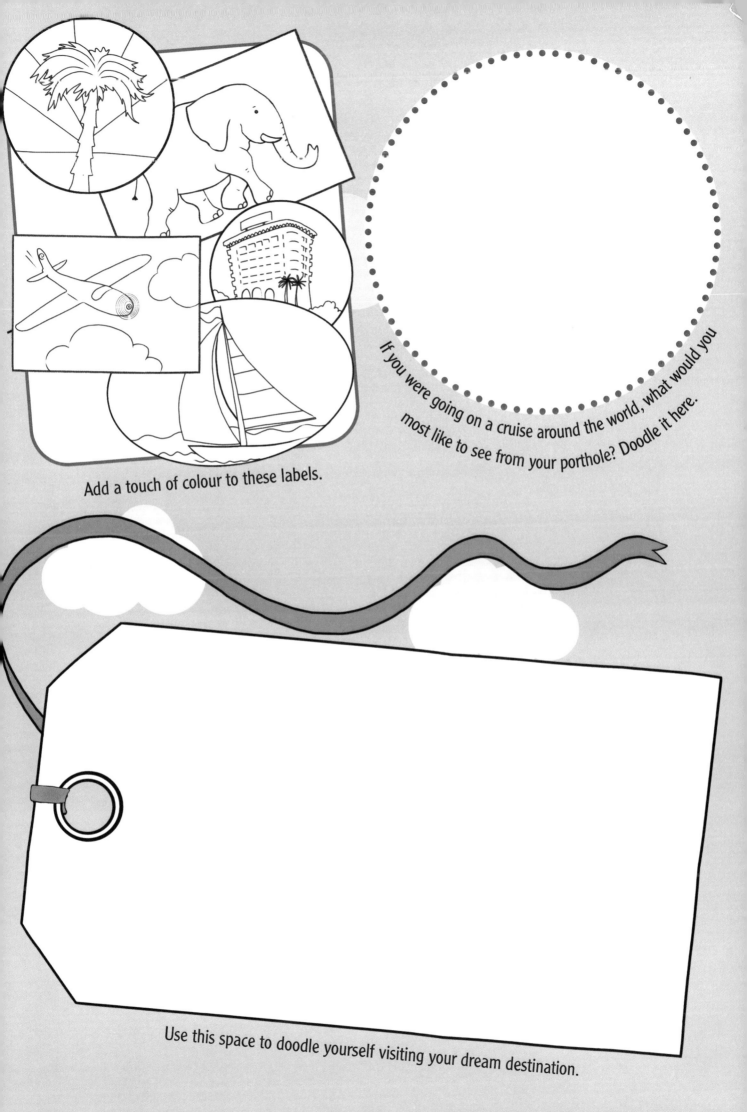

Add a touch of colour to these labels.

If you were going on a cruise around the world, what would you most like to see from your porthole? Doodle it here.

Use this space to doodle yourself visiting your dream destination.

A Garden of Treasures

Like anyone, you probably have lots and lots of stuff. Some of it might be on your floor, or under your bed, but which of your possessions do you truly treasure?

Use these pages to record which of your things you love most and would like to keep for a lifetime – whether it's a special photo, a memory, a favourite book, a game or a song you love.

Either glue in a photo, or doodle a picture of each item.

Use this space to design your own chest of treasure.

Add colour to the plants in your garden of treasures.

Winter Wonderland

The winter months are full of fun things to do — whether you spend cosy nights at home with your family or head out together, wrapped up in hats, scarves and gloves. What are your favourite things about winter? Give this page your own wintry touches.

Add the swirls of the skaters' skates on the ice.

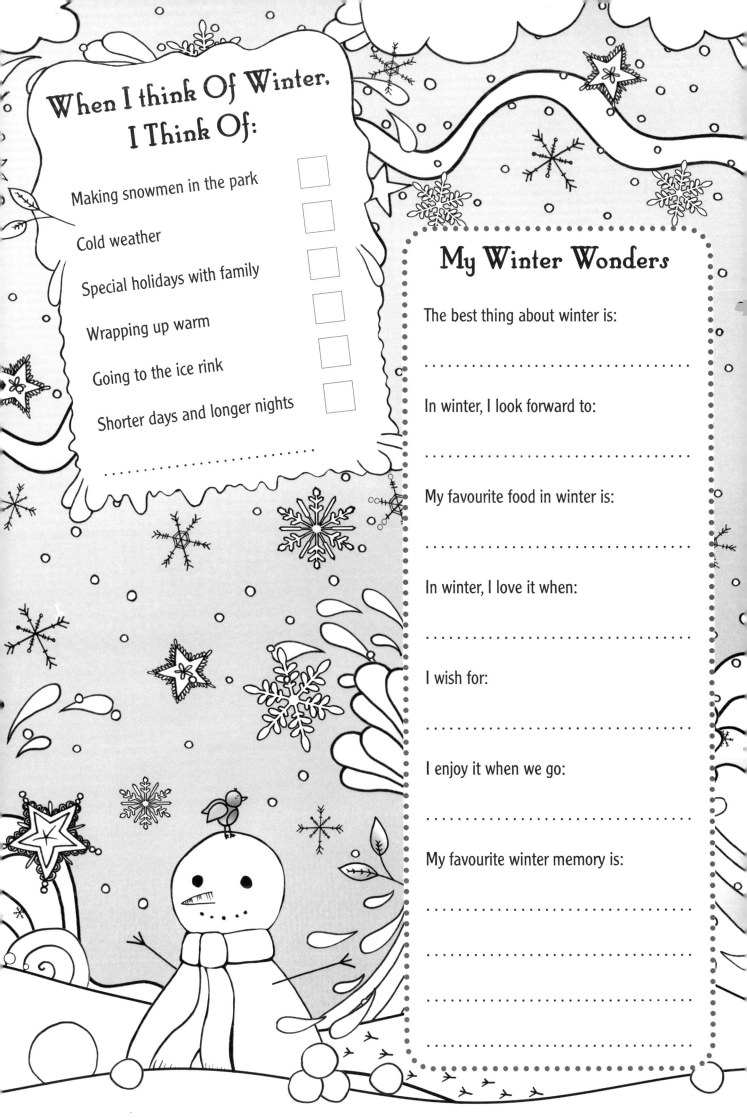

When I think Of Winter, I Think Of:

Making snowmen in the park ☐

Cold weather ☐

Special holidays with family ☐

Wrapping up warm ☐

Going to the ice rink ☐

Shorter days and longer nights ☐

. . . .

My Winter Wonders

The best thing about winter is:

. . . .

In winter, I look forward to:

. . . .

My favourite food in winter is:

. . . .

In winter, I love it when:

. . . .

I wish for:

. . . .

I enjoy it when we go:

. . . .

My favourite winter memory is:

. . . .

. . . .

. . . .

. . . .

Pet Perfect

Whether you're the proud owner of a puppy, a hamster or a kitten, or secretly wish for a pet of your own, this is the place to put pen to paper to record everything about your perfect pet – real or imaginary! Finish the page with all your favourite colours.

What Is Your Dream Pet?

....

Doodle your dream pet here.

Colour the background in your favourite shades.

Which Of These Animals Do You Love Most?

Cats ☐

Dogs ☐

Mice ☐

Rats ☐

Rabbits ☐

Goldfish ☐

Birds ☐

Reptiles ☐

Hamsters ☐

Ponies ☐

Guinea Pigs ☐

☐

....

KITTY

I Would Call My Dream Pet:

....

Glue a photo of you and your pet here. If you haven't got a pet, glue a picture of your favourite animal here instead.

Just Imagine

If I could be any animal, I'd be:

....

I would be called:

....

I would spend every day:

....

I would eat nothing but:

....

I would live in a:

....

I would live with:

....

Wish Upon A Star!

Perhaps you're hoping you'll win a prize at school next week, or that you'll bump into your favourite superstar on the high street, or that you grow up to be prime minister? Whatever you secretly wish for, use this page to make a record, and wait to see if it comes true.

Write down all of your wishes on a piece of paper. Place them in an envelope and glue it shut.

Why not decorate the outside of your envelope, then glue it here, so that your wish is never forgotten.

First published in Great Britain in 2011 by Buster Books, an imprint of Michael O'Mara Books Limited,
9 Lion Yard, Tremadoc Road, London SW4 7NQ

Copyright © Buster Books 2011

ISBN: 978-1-907151-34-7

2 4 6 8 10 9 7 5 3 1

www.mombooks.com/busterbooks

Printed and bound in June 2011 by Tien Wah Press Ltd,
4 Pandan Crescent, Singapore, 128 475.